Relaxing as F_ ck

The Sweary Word Puzzle Book (For Adults)

POP PRESS

Did you know that swearing is good for you?

In 2009, academics in the department of psychology at Keele University, England, carried out a study that concluded that firing off some choice expletives while undergoing a painful experience increased participants' ability to tolerate pain.

This is not surprising. Modern life is stressful and we all need to let off some steam sometimes. And what better way to do it than to embrace the many opportunities our wonderful language gives us to say something naughty. However, it's also true that having an absolute shit fit outside the supermarket or on your morning commute is rather frowned upon. Perhaps for obvious reasons. This is where *The Sweary Word Puzzle Book* comes in.

In these pages, you will find many sweary word games to test the mind and bring you a sense of calm. Cursing is not big and it's not clever, we were told. Well, crack these puzzles to prove otherwise! It is entirely possible to be a potty-mouthed smart arse, it turns out. Answers are can be found on pages 109–23.

From 'cros-swear-ds' to wordoku, anagrams to word ladders and many more besides, this is the very adult yet joyfully immature puzzle book you never knew you needed.

Every Other Letter

Restore the missing letters below, one per gap, to reveal a word whose second part might be chicken or gold.

_ U _ K _ U _ G _ T

Solution on page 110

Wordoku

Place D, E, G, O, R or T into each empty square, so that no letter repeats in any row, column or bold-lined 3×2 box. Once complete, read left to right across the shaded diagonal to reveal something you should generally keep to yourself, if you have one.

	E	R		D	
D					E
					T
O					
G					O
	D		T	G	

Solution on page 110

All Messed Up

Rearrange the following letters to form an 11-letter word that sounds, quite frankly, like an absolute nightmare.

SUCKERFLUCT

Solution on page 110

Cros-swear-ds

Solve the crossword and then rearrange the letters in the shaded squares to reveal a two-word phrase used to describe someone who likes the occasional drink.

Across
1 TV breaks (3)
3 Begin (5)
6 Subject (5)
7 Karate proficiency level (3)
8 Rigorous (9)
9 Place of higher education (3)
10 Something of value (5)
12 Muscular (5)
13 Not bright (3)

Down
1 Part of a play (3)
2 Oversee (9)
3 Subsidiary (9)
4 With a destination written on (9)
5 Core belief (5)
8 Small firework (5)
11 Male cat (3)

Solution on page 110

6

Letter Pairs

Delete one letter from each pair in order to reveal something, though you might want to remove the evidence when you're done.

DW AI CS
KN TS PR
LI OA TN

Solution on page 111

Missing Vowels

Which masterfully sweary insult has had all of its vowels removed? The rear part of the name is a wild animal and the front part is . . . well, also a rear part.

RSWSL

Solution on page 111

'I'm sorry I got angry and said a load of shit I meant, but probably should have kept to myself.'

Picture Poser

Can you sniff out what this picture indicates?
Spoiler: it's definitely not something you'd want to
keep in the fridge.

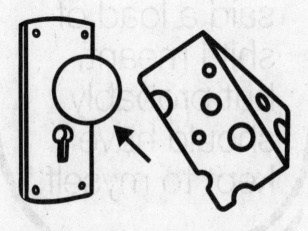

Solution on page 111

Word Sqwears

Travel between adjacent letters to reveal a three-word expression requesting, very respectfully, that you chill out for a moment. Your route should visit all letters exactly once but **may not** travel diagonally.

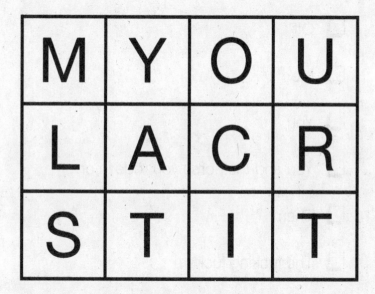

M	Y	O	U
L	A	C	R
S	T	I	T

Solution on page 111

FUCK BINGO

Tick the variation of 'fuck' off the list as you work each into colourful conversation and correspondence:

- ☐ Off
- ☐ Me
- ☐ You
- ☐ You and the horse you rode in on
- ☐ Them
- ☐ The fucking fuckers
- ☐ This shit
- ☐ This for a game of soldiers
- ☐ Everything

Word Ladder

Complete this NSFW word chain by writing a common English word at each step. Each word must use the exact same letters in the same order as the word above, except with a single letter changed. For example, TIT > PIT > PUT > PUN.

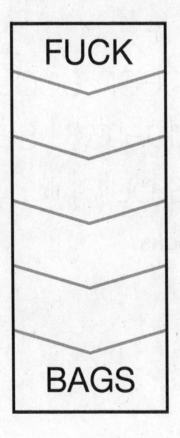

FUCK

BAGS

Solution on page 111

'I've been accused
of vulgarity. I say
that's bullshit.'

Mel Brooks

Initial Fun

Replace each of the three clues below with an equivalent two-letter symbol, then write those two-letter symbols in the spaces provided. Then run around loudly shouting the result*:

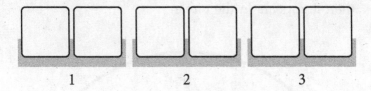

1   2   3

1. Copper (as a chemical element)

2. Megabyte

3. Silver (as a chemical element)

* Probably not wise

Solution on page 111

Word Circles

Rearrange the following letters to reveal something that is highly unlikely to be true.

Then, for a bonus, how many other words can you find that use the centre letter plus two or more of the other letters? No letter may be used more times than it appears in the circle.

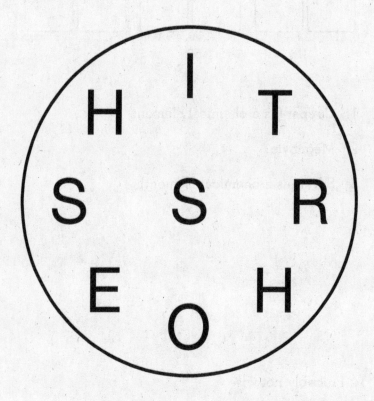

Solution on page 111

Understanding Apostrophes (the sweary way)

The apostrophe is possibly the punctuation mark that most flummoxes us. This is where bad language can help with good grammar.

Add the missing apostrophe to correct the sweary phrases below.

Shits about to hit the fan

For fucks sake

Shits and giggles

I don't give a rats arse

The wazzocks forgotten again

He's off round his fuckbuddys house

Solution on page 112

All Messed Up

Rearrange the following letters to form a 3-word phrase (2, 4, 8) which you might use when solving puzzles (or mysterious crimes) with dumb friends.

OH! SLOTH NICKERS

Solution on page 112

Word Ladder

Complete this NSFW word chain by writing a common English word at each step. Each word must use the exact same letters in the same order as the word above, except with a single letter changed. For example, TIT > PIT > PUT > PUN.

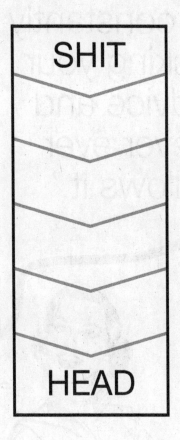

SHIT

HEAD

Solution on page 112

Sworn Secrets

Insert a sweary word into the gap provided to reveal a common English word, writing one letter per underline. For example, you could add SHIT to MI_ _ _ _S to reveal MISHITS.

CO_ _ _ _ _LY

Solution on page 112

The Curious Meanings of Animal Shit

To English speakers, the combination of an animal with its shit has a very particular meaning, depending on which creature's excrement is being referenced. Match the 'shit' to the definition:

Horse   Lies

Bull   Fearful

Ape   Crazy or illogical

Dog   Nonsense

Chicken   Angry or aggressive

Bat   Poor quality

Solution on page 112

Missing Vowels

Which sweary term, referring to a lack of
sportsmanship and some underhand conduct, has
had all of its vowels removed?

SHTHSRY

Solution on page 112

Word Sqwears

Travel between adjacent letters to reveal a three-word expression meaning 'fun and games' – how appropriate. Your route should visit all letters exactly once but **may not** travel diagonally between them.

S	T	S	D	G
H	I	A	N	I
S	E	L	G	G

Solution on page 112

Finish This

You've been playing a word game and you're down to your last guess. Maybe your previous attempts were a bit childish, but there's only one possible word left. Black squares show incorrect letters; grey squares are correct letters in the wrong positions. The white square is a correct letter in the correct position.

What is the correct word?

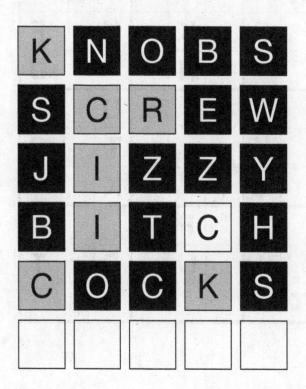

Solution on page 113

Wordoku

Place C, F, H, I, K, N, S, T or U into each empty square, so that no letter repeats in any row, column or bold-lined 3×3 box. Once complete, read left to right across the shaded diagonal to reveal an undesirable companion.

	H						K	
I		S		K		N		F
T				N				U
		T			N	U		
H		K				T		C
		U	I			K		
K				F				N
S		I		U		F		T
	T						S	

Solution on page 113

Picture Poser

What annoying person do you think this innocent-seeming picture shows? Then, after you've figured it out, can you spot another sweary word hiding inside the solution?

Solution on page 113

Every Other Letter

1. Restore the missing letters below, one per gap, to reveal a word which is something you probably don't want to receive after a stressful day:

$$\_O\_L\_C\_I\_G$$

Solution on page 113

Fucking Acronyms

Short of time in which to express your thoughts?
It might be quicker to use these acronyms instead.
But do you know what they stand for?

SFA

FFS

GFY

NFI

JFGI

NMFP

STFU

LMFAO

NMFLTG

Solution on pages 113–14

Word Circle

Rearrange the following letters to reveal a person who thinks very highly of themselves, but who absolutely shouldn't.

Then, for a bonus, how many other words can you find that use the centre letter plus two or more of the other letters? No letter may be used more times than it appears in the circle.

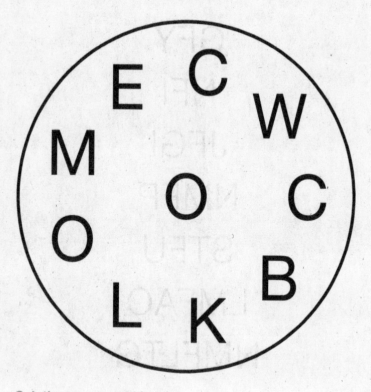

Solution on page 114

All Messed Up

Rearrange the following letters to form a 3-word phrase (1, 6, 4) that, depending on your mood, you might not give.

AN IFFY GLUCK

Solution on page 114

Sworn Secrets

Insert a sweary word into the gap provided to reveal a common English word, writing one letter per underline. For example, you could add SHIT to MI_ _ _ _S to reveal MISHITS.

LA_ _ _UDE

Solution on page 114

'You have to
know how to be
vulgar. Paint with
four-letter words.'

Pablo Picasso

Sworn Secrets

Insert a sweary word into the gap provided to reveal a common English word, writing one letter per underline. For example, you could add SHIT to MI_ _ _ _S to reveal MISHITS.

SMAR_ _ _ _ _CH

Solution on page 114

Cros-swear-ds

Solve the crossword and then rearrange the letters in the shaded squares to reveal a hidden word for something which is, frankly, a complete disaster.

Across
1 Substituted (8)
5 Slime (3)
6 Afternoon drink, informally (3)
8 Attractive young woman (5)
9 Need to pay back (3)
10 Doze (3)
11 Thin bed covering (5)
12 Bro's opposite (3)
13 Greek letter representing density (3)
14 Toddler's pedal vehicle (8)

Down
1 Territories (7)
2 Food blender (9)
3 Pleasing in appearance (9)
4 Strange, as in behaviour (9)
7 Sanction (7)

Solution on page 114

Letter Pairs

Delete one letter from each pair to reveal a unit of measurement which may or may not be metric:

SF HU EC
RK - TI
OR SN

Solution on page 115

Word Sqwears

Travel between letters to reveal a hopefully non-literal adjective to describe someone who might have drunk a few too many, er, lemonades. Your route should visit all of the letters exactly once and **may** move diagonally between letters.

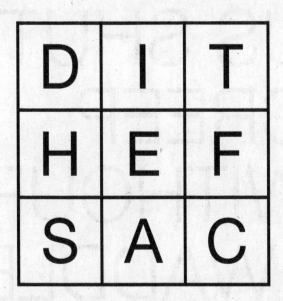

Solution on page 115

Idioms

In a sticky situation? Change exactly one letter in each word to reveal a place you might sometimes inadvertently find yourself:

US SHUT CREEP WITHOUR I WADDLE

Solution on page 115

SHIT BINGO

Tick the variation of 'shit' off the list as you work each into colourful conversation and correspondence:

- ❑ ! Hot
- ❑ ?! For brains
- ❑ # Sandwich
- ❑ ! Stirrer
- ❑ !? Faced
- ❑ # The bed
- ❑ ! A brick
- ❑ ?! Happens
- ❑ # Or get off the can

Missing vowels

Which insult has had all of its vowels removed below? Both parts of the word are anatomical(ish) terms, though only about half of the population has the first part.

TWTNS

Solution on page 115

'Let us swear while we may, for in heaven it will not be allowed.'

Mark Twain

Word Ladder

Complete this NSFW word chain by writing a common English word at each step. Each word must use the exact same letters in the same order as the word above, except with a single letter changed. For example, TIT > PIT > PUT > PUN.

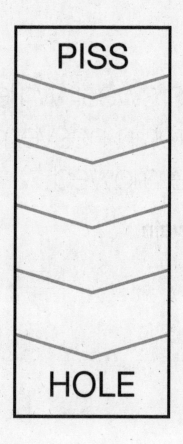

PISS

HOLE

Solution on page 115

43

All Messed Up

Rearrange the following letters to form a classic 8-letter insult, constructed of two anatomical words.

HA! BONKED

Solution on page 115

Cros-swear-d

Solve the crossword and then rearrange the letters
in the shaded squares to reveal a hidden word
used to describe a thoroughly unpleasant person.

Across
1 Using base ten (7)
6 No score (3)
7 Tomb (5)
8 Referred to (9)
10 South American beaver-like rodent (5)
12 Seize (3)
13 Grapple in a fight (7)

Down
1 Kinetics (8)
2 Punctuation mark (5)
3 Size (9)
4 Grazing land (3)
5 Legible (8)
9 Nine-voice group (5)
11 Evergreen tree with red berries (3)

Solution on page 115

Every Other Letter

Restore the missing letters below, one per gap, to reveal a word befitting an unlucky character from Greek tragedy:

_O_H_R_U_K_R

Solution on page 115

Idioms

Want to show your appreciation? Change one letter in each word to reveal an expression of sincere gratitude:

THINK TUCK FAR WHAT

Solution on page 116

Picture Poser

Can you find out what annoying thing these pictures represent? In case you get stuck, you should know that it's all complete rubbish anyway.

Solution on page 116

Sworn Secrets

Insert a sweary word into the gap provided to reveal a common English word, writing one letter per underline. For example, you could add SHIT to MI_ _ _ _S to reveal MISHITS.

B_ _ _ _LINE

Solution on page 116

Wordoku

Place A, D, E, H, I, K, S, T or W into each empty square, so that no letter repeats in any row, column or bold-lined 3×3 box. Once complete, read left to right across the shaded diagonal to reveal something worthless.

		K				W		
		T		D		E		
A	E						S	D
		H		W	I	D		
	T		A		K		I	
		A	D	S		K		
K	I						D	H
		D		K		S		
		W			I			

Solution on page 116

Shit By Quantity

Order these measurements of an amount of shit from small to large.

Deep shit • A pile of shit • A mountain of shit • A piece of shit • A load of shit • A ton of shit • A crock of shit • Full of shit

_____

_____

_____

_____

_____

_____

_____

_____

Solution on page 116

Missing Vowels

Which cheerful, affirmative expression has had all of the vowels removed below?

BSFCKNGLTLY

Solution on page 117

Word Sqwears

Travel between letters to reveal a word used to describe a person who's not in your good books. Your route should visit all of the letters exactly once and **may** travel diagonally between letters.

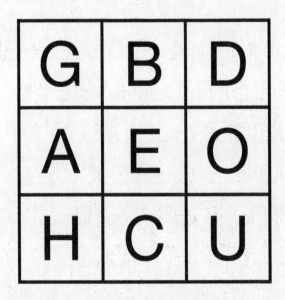

Solution on page 117

'Vulgarity is a necessary part of a complete author's equipment; and the clown is sometimes the best part of the circus.'

George Bernard Shaw

Sworn Secrets

Insert a sweary word into the gap provided to reveal a common English word, writing one letter per underline. For example, you could add SHIT to MI_ _ _ _S to reveal MISHITS.

S_ _ _ _ _IEST

Solution on page 117

Sworn Secrets

Insert a sweary word into the gap provided to reveal a common English word, writing one letter per underline. For example, you could add SHIT to MI_ _ _S to reveal MISHITS.

SA_ _ _ _AY

Solution on page 117

The Most Versatile Word in the English Language?

Fuck (and its variants) can bend itself into almost any grammatical form: noun, plural noun, verb (transitive), verb (intransitive), adverb . . . Find a form of fuck to complete the phrases below.

What the _____ do I know?

What is this mad _____?

The dumb _____ is at it again

I have no more _____ to give

This whisk is _____

I find him strangely _____

Let's _____ this shit up

He completely _____ him over

Continues overleaf

They _____ vigorously

He _____ around

I don't _____ know

That was a _____ dogshit

Isn't grammar fun?! Now identify the noun, adjective and verb:

Fuck the fucking fuckers

Noun_____

Adjective_____

Verb_____

Solutions on page 117

All Messed Up

Rearrange the following letters to form a 9-letter word that you should probably clean up before you head out.

WANT A SINK?

Solution on page 118

Cros-swear-d

Solve the crossword and then rearrange the letters in the shaded squares to reveal a hidden word where the first section is a body part and the second is a foodstuff. Sounds yummy . . .

Across
1 Tempting (8)
5 Decorative pond fish (3)
6 Living creature (5)
8 Late in paying money (2,7)
10 Ground (5)
13 Lubricate (3)
15 Elevated (8)

Down
1 Bug (3)
2 'Behold!' (5)
3 Wrath (3)
4 Knowledge (3)
6 Lineage (5)
7 Oxygen or nitrogen, eg (3)
8 Barman's query (3)
9 Circa (5)
11 Guitar loudspeaker (3)
12 Moreover (3)
14 Young man (3)

Solution on page 118

Idioms

Change one letter in each word to reveal an occasion on which you might want to be absent, if you possibly can:

THEN SHE SKIT HUTS TIE FUN

Solution on page 118

Picture Poser

1. Have some family fun working out what this picture indicates. Only about half of the population have one of these, and they wouldn't want to crush them.

Solution on page 118

Sworn Secrets

Insert a sweary word into the gap provided to reveal a common English word, writing one letter per underline. For example, you could add SHIT to MI_ _ _ _S to reveal MISHITS.

GOOSE_ _ _P

Solution on page 118

Word Circle

Rearrange the following letters to reveal a word you might use to describe an act of highly impressive stupidity.

Then, for a bonus, how many other words can you find that use the centre letter plus two or more of the other letters? No letter may be used more times than it appears in the circle.

Solution on page 118

Finish This

You've been playing a word game and you're down to your last guess. Maybe your previous attempts were a bit suggestive, but there's only one possible word left. Black squares show incorrect letters; grey squares are correct letters in the wrong positions. The white squares are correct letters in the correct positions.

What appropriate word is revealed?

Solution on page 119

ARSE BINGO

Tick the variation of 'arse' off the list as you work each into colourful conversation and correspondence:

- ☐ Hole
- ☐ Hat
- ☐ About face
- ☐ Over tit
- ☐ Kicking
- ☐ Lick
- ☐ Bastard
- ☐ Biscuits
- ☐ Goblin

Wordoku

Place A, E, H, L, O, S, T or W into each empty square, so that no letter repeats in any row, column or bold-lined 4×2 box. Once complete, read left to right across the shaded diagonal to reveal an interesting entry.

	O					A	
A		H			E		O
	S		E	L		O	
		W			A		
		O			L		
	T		H	S		E	
E		T			S		H
	H					T	

Letter Pairs

Delete one letter from each pair to reveal a non-technical, but mildly amusing, name for a part of the male anatomy:

SD AC RH
LR AO EN
KG

Solution on page 119

'Cursing is not simply a childish preoccupation with profanity, it's a sign of an age-old love affair with the intricacies and nuances of our native tongue.'

Susie Dent

Idioms

Change one letter in each word to reveal a phrase used to describe someone demonstrating an admirable sense of zen:

HERO
FUNKS
GIVER

Solution on page 119

Word Ladder

Complete this NSFW word chain by writing a common English word at each step. Each word must use the exact same letters in the same order as the word above, except with a single letter changed. For example, TIT > PIT > PUT > PUN.

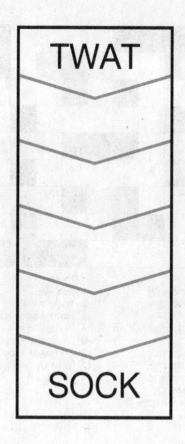

TWAT

SOCK

Solution on page 119

Cros-swear-d

Solve the crossword and then rearrange the letters in the shaded squares to reveal a hidden word that could be used to describe a person who has a special way of looking at the world, often followed by 'crazy'.

Across
1 TV programme (4)
4 Edible kernel (3)
5 Look at (3)
6 Float gently up and down (3)
8 Shadow (5)
9 Get it wrong (3)
10 Odd; peculiar (3)
11 Make a change to (5)
13 The whole lot (3)
15 Seventh Greek letter (3)
16 Swindle (3)
17 Finishes (4)

Down
1 Butt (4)
2 Try to win (3)
3 Former Spanish currency (6)
4 Pertaining to a nerve (6)
6 Bleak and lifeless (6)
7 Complain about (6)
12 Nervous twitches (4)
14 Shelter (3)

Solution on page 120

'Vulgarity is the garlic in the salad of taste.'

Cyril Connolly

Letter Pairs

Delete one letter from each pair to reveal a timeless, catch-all insult:

WG LA EN CK ES RN

Solution on page 120

Understanding Prepositions with Swears

Just in case your grammar is a little rusty, a preposition is a word that indicates location, direction, spatial relationship or time. They are the most often used words in the English language (well, depending on how annoyed you are).

Use each of the following prepositions **only once** to form six recognisable phrases below:

up off into over about on

to shit _____

to fuck _____

to fanny _____

to wank _____

to piss _____

to toss _____

Solution on page 120

Idioms

Change one letter in each word to reveal a
motivational message that might just help you turn
your day around:

WET TOUR SUIT TOFETHER

Solution on page 120

Finish This

You've been playing a word game and you're down to your last guess. Maybe your previous attempts were a bit suggestive, but there's only one possible word left. Black squares show incorrect letters; grey squares are correct letters in the wrong positions.

What is the word? It's a verb often followed by '-ING' when describing a certain behaviour.

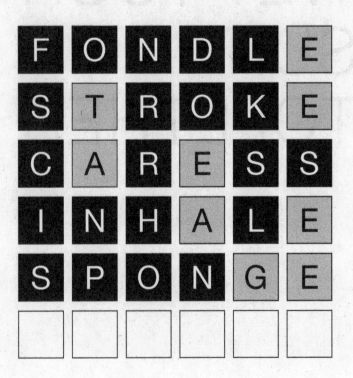

F	O	N	D	L	E
S	T	R	O	K	E
C	A	R	E	S	S
I	N	H	A	L	E
S	P	O	N	G	E

Solution on page 120

Sworn Secret

Insert a sweary word into the gap provided to reveal a common English word, writing one letter per underline. For example, you could add SHIT to MI_ _ _ _S to reveal MISHITS.

CROS_ _ _ _CH

Solution on page 121

Word Sqwears

Travel between letters to reveal a hidden word. Your route should visit all of the letters exactly once and **may** travel diagonally between letters. Got an omnishambles on your hands? You're probably seeing a lot of this too:

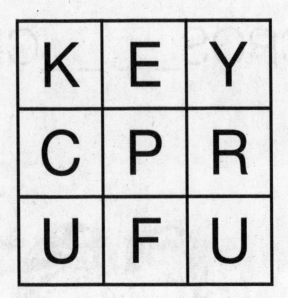

Solution on page 121

Picture Poser

Why not spend a few happy moments working out what this picture indicates? It's part of an item of anatomy owned by roughly 50 per cent of the population:

Solution on page 121

Every Other Letter

Restore the missing letters below, one per gap, to reveal a fictional place that you'll probably never want to travel to:

_ H _ T _ V _ L _ E

Solution on page 121

'When a gentleman is disposed to swear, it is not for any standers-by to curtail his oaths.'

William Shakespeare

Sworn Secrets

Insert a sweary word into the gap provided to reveal a common English word, writing one letter per underline. For example, you could add SHIT to MI_ _ _ _S to reveal MISHITS.

S_ _ _ _BOOK

Solution on page 121

Word Circles

Rearrange the following letters to reveal somewhere you might not want to hang around.

Then, for a bonus, how many other words can you find that use the centre letter plus two or more of the other letters? No letter may be used more times than it appears in the circle.

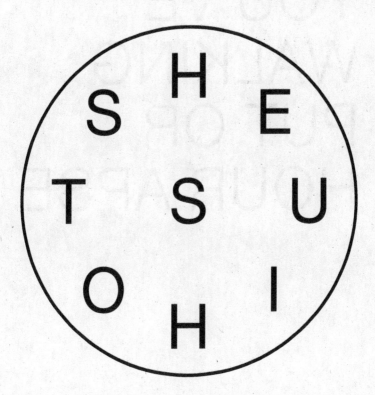

Solution on page 121

Idioms

Change one letter in each word to reveal a phrase you might use to point out that someone is not quite making sense:

YOU'VE WALKING PUT OR HOUR APSE

Solution on page 121

Word Ladder

Complete this NSFW word chain by writing a common English word at each step. Each word must use the exact same letters in the same order as the word above, except with a single letter changed. For example, TIT > PIT > PUT > PUN.

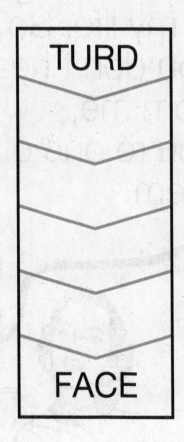

TURD

FACE

Solution on page 121

Sworn Secrets

Insert a sweary word into the gap provided to reveal a common English word, writing one letter per underline. For example, you could add SHIT to MI_ _ _ _S to reveal MISHITS.

DI_ _ _ _AL

Solution on page 121

International Offence

Let's take a moment to celebrate some expletive belters in other languages. Never be lost for an insult, wherever you are.

'Na mou klaseis ta'rxidia!'

Greek. 'Fart on my balls!' A way of dismissing someone as weak and ineffective.

'Kon da ti go natrese!'

Bulgarian. 'Get fucked by a horse!' Not particularly elegant but fairly self-explanatory – 'Go fuck yourself', basically.

'Tofu no kado ni atama wo butsukete shine!'

Japanese. 'Hit your head on a corner of tofu and die!' Relatively tame but pleasingly odd in translation.

'Gay kocken offen yom!'

Yiddish. 'Go shit in the ocean!' A neat dismissal.

'Niú bī!'

Chinese. Used by the young to mean awesome or great. The litteral translation is 'cow vagina'.

'Me cago en la leche!'

Spanish. An expression of annoyance, irritation or unwelcome surprise. Literally: 'I shit in the milk.'

'Go n-ithe an cat thú is go n-ithe an diabhal an cat.'

Irish. Though probably among the world's most prolific and gleeful swearers, the Irish actually don't need curse words to cut someone down to size. This means 'May the cat eat you and may the devil eat the cat.'

'Swearing was invented as a compromise between running away and fighting.'

Finley Peter Dunne

Cros-swear-d

Solve the crossword and then rearrange the letters in the shaded squares to reveal a hidden word which can be used to describe less-than-helpful behaviour.

Across

1 Quality that surrounds a person (4)
4 Fragrant, prickly flower (4)
7 Cross-dressing (4)
8 Troubles (4)
9 Aptness (9)
12 Journeyed by horse (4)
14 Strike with the foot (4)
16 'Sure!' (4)
17 Twirl (4)

Down

1 Lend a hand (3)
2 Quarrel (5)
3 Letter following chi (3)
5 Vivacity (4)
6 Cay (4)
9 Few and far between (4)
10 Woman (4)
11 Egyptian crosses (5)
13 Expression of horror (3)
15 Knowledge (3)

Solution on page 122

Idioms

Change one letter in each word to reveal a helpful question, suitable for anyone possibly stating the obvious:

GOES I BEAT SHIP IF TOE FOODS?

Solution on page 122

'What I'm saying
maybe profane
but it's also
profound.'

Richard Pryor

Wordoku

Place A, B, C, E, F, H, I, S or T into each empty square, so that no letter repeats in any row, column or bold-lined 3×3 box. Once complete, read left to right across the shaded diagonal to reveal something that may be 'resting'.

		H		T		I		
			H		S			
	S		E		I		B	
T								I
I			T		B			A
	T			E			H	
S			A	I	H			F
		C				B		

Solution on page 122

Idioms

Change one letter in each word to reveal a description for someone who may not deliver on their promises:

AIL FARM ANY SO SPIT

Solution on page 123

Ambiguity

Our favourite swears are generally multipurpose, with the result that their implications are not always clear cut. What can mean:

- to have an affair OR waste time

- a testicle OR to tell off

- to fornicate OR a seabird

- to leave OR to annoy

- to have hit something / to be very drunk

Solution on page 123

Every Other Letter

Restore the missing letters below, one per gap, to reveal a word whose second part might be chicken or gold:

_U_K_U_G_T

Solution on page 123

Word Ladder

Complete this NSFW word chain by writing a common English word at each step. Each word must use the exact same letters in the same order as the word above, except with a single letter changed. For example, TIT > PIT > PUT > PUN.

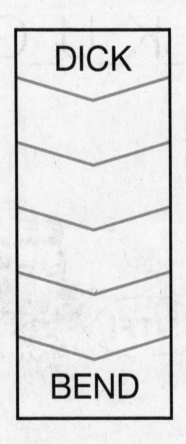

DICK

BEND

Solution on page 123

Understanding the Reflexive with Swears

The reflexive denotes something one does to oneself. Or, the person on the receiving end of the act is also the one doing it.

Can you fill in the blanks to make these phrases reflexive using the words from the list: pissed, twatted, shat, fucked.

- She did three marathons and totally _____ _____

- He _____ _____ when his boss appeared

- She _____ _____ laughing

- He _____ _____ on the head with his own badminton racket

Can you think of anything else you might do to yourself?

Solution on page 123

Fucking Anagrams

Nothing beats a short, sharp shock for bringing out our best swearing. Unscramble the below to reveal some common and profane exclamations of surprise.

chatbiirks!

(4, 1, 5)

brichkeinaseot!

(6, 2, 1, 4)

fumyesiewdacks!

(4, 2, 8)

ufdcacukk!

(4, 1, 4)

Solution on page 123

Build Your Own Expletive

Here are a few possible two-word combinations to help you express your stress:

Fuck	Womble
Fanny	Trumpet
Knob	Flaps
Fart	Muppet
Minge	Bucket
Cock	Goblin
Arse	Tits

'Grant me some wild
expressions, Heavens,
or I shall burst.'

George Farquhar

Naughty Alter Egos

Using the first letters of your first and last name, create either a devilish alter ego for yourself or a secret nickname for someone you are not too fond of . . .

Eg, if your name is Joe Bloggs, your new name would be 'Jizzy Big Bollocks'.

Arsewipe	Arsington
Ballsack	Big Bollocks
Cocker	Cumbag
Dickwad	Le Douche
Effing	Elephant dong
Fuckface	Flaps
Gobshite	Git
Hairy Arse	Horseshit
Itchy	Idiot
Jizzy	Jackass
Knobby	Knobcheese
Lechy	Limpdick
Mofo	McShite
Nutsack	Nugget

Omnifucker	Otter
Pussy	Pisspants
Queefer	Quim
Roger	Rat-arsed
Shithead	Scrote
Tosser	Turd
Unclefucker	Uglyfuck
Vommy	Vajazzle
Wanky	Wetwipe
X-rated	XXX
Y-fronts	Yoghurt
Zitty	Zero fucks

Idioms

Change and rearrange some letters to reveal a
description for feeling unpleasant after a night of
socialising.

TOUGH IS A GRABEDS IRSE

Solution on page 123

Here are the fucking answers!

p3. FUCKNUGGET

p4. TODGER

T	E	R	O	D	G
D	O	G	R	T	E
R	G	D	E	O	T
O	T	E	G	R	D
G	R	T	D	E	O
E	D	O	T	G	R

p5. CLUSTERFUCK

p6. The hidden phrase is PISS ARTIST

p7. DICKSPLAT

p8. ARSEWEASEL

p10. KNOB CHEESE

p11. CALM YOUR TITS

p13. FUCK BUCK BACK BASK BASS BAGS

p15.
1. The chemical element Copper can be written as Cu
2. Megabyte is abbreviated to MB
3. The chemical element Silver can be written as Ag

Writing these letters in the boxes reveals CUMBAG

p16. HORSESHIT
Other words to find include: ethos, heirs, hers, hies, hires, his, hiss, hits, hoes, hoist, hoists, horse, horses, horsiest, hose, hoses, host, hosts, its, ohs, ores, osier, osiers, others, resist, rest, rests, riots, rise, rises, rites, roes, rose, roses, rosiest, rotes, rots, set, sets, she, shies, shire, shires, shirt, shirts, shoe, shoes, shore, shores, short, shortish, shorts, shot, shots, sir, sire, sires, sirs, sis, sister, sit, site, sites, sits, sore, sores, sorest, sort, sortie, sorties, sorts, sties, stir, stirs, store, stores, stories, theirs, thesis, this, those, thresh, throes, tiers, ties, tires, toes, tors, toss, tress, tries, trios

p17.

Shit's about to hit the fan

For fuck's sake

Shits and giggles (trick question!)

I don't give a rat's arse

The wazzock's forgotten again

He's off round his fuckbuddy's house

p18. NO SHIT, SHERLOCK

p19. SHIT SPIT SPAT SEAT HEAT HEAD

p21. ARSE: COARSELY

p22.

Horseshit	Nonsense
Bullshit	Lies
Apeshit	Angry or aggressive
Dogshit	Poor quality
Chickenshit	Fearful
Batshit	Crazy or illogical

p23. SHITHOUSERY

p24. SHITS AND GIGGLES

p25. PRICK

p26. FUCKSTICK

F	H	N	S	T	U	C	K	I
I	U	S	C	K	H	N	T	F
T	K	C	F	N	I	S	H	U
C	F	T	K	H	N	U	I	S
H	I	K	U	S	F	T	N	C
N	S	U	I	C	T	K	F	H
K	C	H	T	F	S	I	U	N
S	N	I	H	U	K	F	C	T
U	T	F	N	I	C	H	S	K

p27. Asshat – which also contains a hidden 'shat'! (as**shat**)

p28. BOLLOCKING

p29.

SFA	Sweet fuck all
FFS	For fuck's sake
GFY	Go fuck yourself
NFI	No fucking idea
JFGI	Just fucking google it
NMFP	Not my fucking problem
STFU	Shut the fuck up

p30. COCKWOMBLE

Other words to find include: below, bloc, block, bloom, blow, bole, boo, book, boom, bow, bowl, clock, cob, cockle, coke, comb, combo, come, coo, cook, cool, cow, cowl, elbow, lob, lobe, lock, loco, look, loom, low, meow, mob, mock, mole, moo, mow, oboe, owe, owl, woe, wok, woke, womb, woo, wool

p31. A FLYING FUCK

p32. TIT: LA<u>TIT</u>UDE

p34. TWAT: SMAR<u>TWAT</u>CH

p35. The hidden word is SHITSHOW.

R	E	P	L	A	C		E	D	
E		R		E		C			
G	O	O		S		C	H	A	
I		C	U	T	I	E		P	
O	W	E		H		N	A	P	
N		S	H	E	E	T		R	
S	I	S		T		R	H	O	
		O		I		I		V	
	T	R	I	C	Y	C	L	E	

p45. The hidden word is BASTARD.

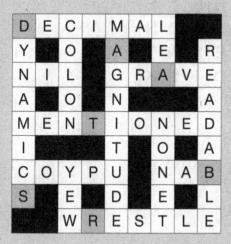

p47. THANK FUCK FOR THAT

p48. Bulls + hit = bullshit

p49. ASS: BASSLINE

p50. SHITEHAWK

S	D	K	E	I	T	W	H	A
W	H	T	S	D	A	E	K	I
A	E	I	K	H	W	T	S	D
E	K	H	T	W	I	D	A	S
D	T	S	A	E	K	H	I	W
I	W	A	D	S	H	K	T	E
K	I	E	W	T	S	A	D	H
H	A	D	I	K	E	S	W	T
T	S	W	H	A	D	I	E	K

p51.

A piece of shit

A pile of shit

A crock of shit

A load of shit

Deep shit

Full of shit

A ton of shit

A mountain of shit

p52. ABSOFUCKINGLUTELY

p53. DOUCHEBAG

p55. WANK: SWANKIEST

p56. TURD: SATURDAY

p57–8. What the fuck do I know?
What is this mad fuckery?
The dumb fuck is at it again.
I have no more fucks to give
The whisk is fucked
I find him strangely fuckable
Let's fuck this shit up
He completely fucked him over
They fucked vigorously
He fucks around
I don't fucking know
That was a fucking dogshit

p58. Verb: Fuck
Adjective: Fucking
Noun: Fuckers

p59. WANKSTAIN

p60. The hidden word is KNOBNOODLE.

p61. WHEN THE SHIT HITS THE FAN

p62. Ballsack

p63. BUM: GOOSEBUMP

p64. DUNDERFUCK

Other words to find include: crude, cud, cue, cued, cur, curd, cure, cured, drunk, duck, ducked, dud, dude, due, duke, duked, dun, dunce, dune, dunk, dunked, ecru, fecund, feud, fun, fund, funded, fur, nude, refund, rude, rue, rued, run, rune, udder, under, undue, urn

p65. WILLY

p67. TWATHOLE

T	O	E	S	W	H	A	L
A	W	H	L	T	E	S	O
H	S	A	E	L	T	O	W
O	L	W	T	E	A	H	S
S	E	O	A	H	L	W	T
W	T	L	H	S	O	E	A
E	A	T	W	O	S	L	H
L	H	S	O	A	W	T	E

p68. SCHLONG

p70. ZERO FUCKS GIVEN

p71. TWAT SWAT SWAP SOAP SOAK SOCK

p72. The hidden word is BATSHIT.

p75. WANKER

p76.

to shit on

to fuck up

to fanny about

to wank over

to piss into

to toss off

p77. GET YOUR SHIT TOGETHER

p78. TEABAG

p79. SHAT: CROS<u>SHAT</u>CH

p80. UPFUCKERY

p81. BELLEND

p82. SHITSVILLE

p84. CRAP: S<u>CRAP</u>BOOK

p85. SHITHOUSE

Other words to find include: ethos, hies, his, hiss, hits, hoes, hoist, hoists, hose, hoses, host, hosts, house, houses, hues, hush, hushes, huts, issue, its, ohs, oust, ousts, outs, set, sets, she, shies, shoe, shoes, shot, shots, shout, shouts, shut, shuts, sis, sit, site, sites, sits, souse, south, sties, sue, sues, suet, suit, suite, suites, suits, sushi, thesis, this, those, thous, thus, ties, tissue, toes, toss, use, uses

p86. YOU'RE TALKING OUT OF YOUR ARSE

p88. TURD CURD CURE CARE FARE FACE

p89. GIT: DI<u>GIT</u>AL

p93. The hidden word is DICKISH

p94. DOES A BEAR SHIT IN THE WOODS?

p96. BITCHFACE

Published in 2023 by Pop Press, an imprint of Ebury Publishing
20 Vauxhall Bridge Road
London SW1V 2SA

Pop Press is part of the Penguin Random House group of companies
whose addresses can be found at global.penguinrandomhouse.com

First published by Pop Press in 2023

www.penguin.co.uk

A CIP catalogue record for this book is available from the British Library

ISBN 9781529927078

Typeset in 13/15pt Beton Std by Jouve (UK), Milton Keynes
Printed and bound in Great Britain by Clays Ltd, Elcograf S.p.A.

The authorised representative in the EEA is Penguin Random House
Ireland, Morrison Chambers, 32 Nassau Street, Dublin D02 YH68

Penguin Random House is committed to a sustainable future
for our business, our readers and our planet. This book is made
from Forest Stewardship Council® certified paper.